AGES 3-5
Preschool

Gold Stars®

Starting to
Read and Write

horse

hen

hay

PaRRagon

Bath · New York · Cologne · Melbourne · Delhi
Hong Kong · Shenzhen · Singapore

Helping your child

⭐ Remember that the activities in this book should be enjoyed by your child. Try to find a quiet place to work.

⭐ Your child does not need to complete each page in one go. Always stop before your child grows tired, and come back to the same page another time.

⭐ It is important to work through the pages in the right order because the activities get progressively more difficult.

⭐ Phonics help children to understand that letters and groups of letters make different sounds. Blending them together makes words. Learning about phonics helps children to read.

⭐ The answers to the activities are on page 24.

⭐ Always give your child lots of encouragement and praise.

⭐ Remember that the gold stars are a reward for effort as well as for achievement.

This edition published by Parragon Books Ltd in 2017

Parragon Books Ltd
Chartist House
15–17 Trim Street
Bath BA1 1HA, UK
www.parragon.com

ISBN 978-1-4748-7119-8

Printed in China

Contents

Trace over the dotted lines. Then make a row underneath.

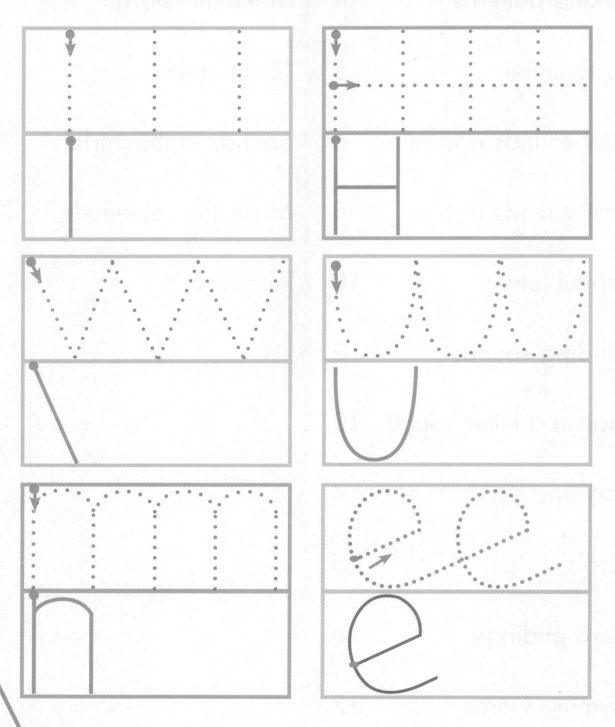

Note for parent: This activity gives practice in pencil control in preparation for letter shapes.

Go together

Start at the red dot. Draw along each path.
Try not to touch the lines.

Note for parent: Keeping between the lines helps pencil control.

5

Letter sounds a to m

Trace over each letter, then circle the two things that start with that letter sound.

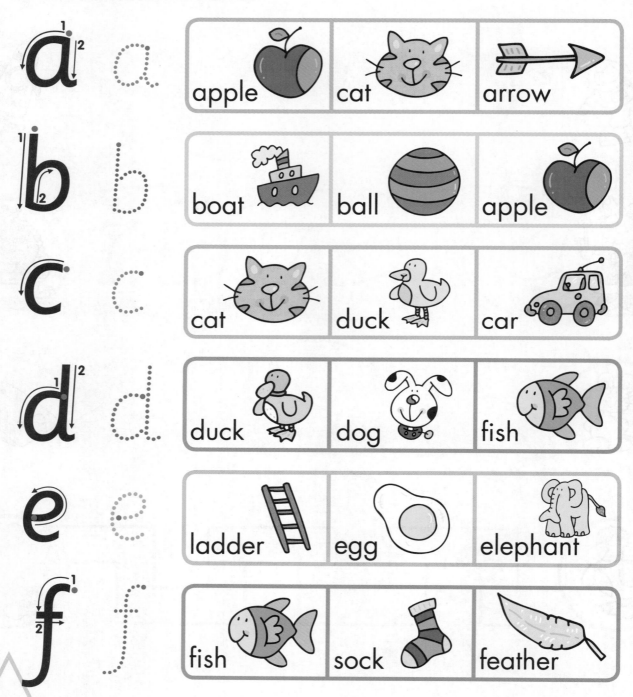

a   a
apple   cat   arrow

b   b
boat   ball   apple

c   c
cat   duck   car

d   d
duck   dog   fish

e   e
ladder   egg   elephant

f   f
fish   sock   feather

Note for parent: This helps children to understand beginning sounds in words.

g   g

goat   gate   rocket

h   h

key   hand   helicopter

i   i

insect   lion   igloo

j   j

jar   juggler   ladybird

k   k

umbrella   key   king

l   l

ladder   car   lion

m   m

mouse   moon   hammer

Letter sounds n to z

Trace over each letter, then circle the two things that start with that letter sound.

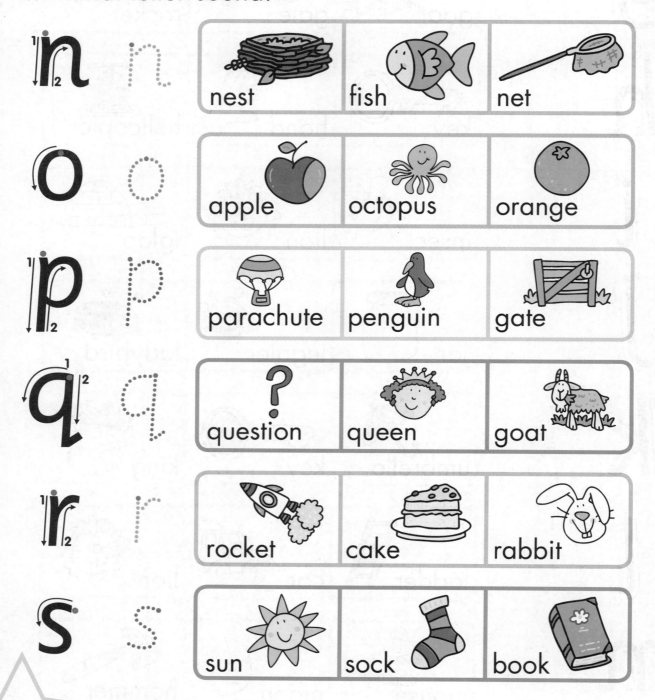

n   n   n

nest   fish   net

o   o   o

apple   octopus   orange

p   p   p

parachute   penguin   gate

q   q   q

question   queen   goat

r   r   r

rocket   cake   rabbit

s   s   s

sun   sock   book

Note for parent: This helps children to understand beginning sounds in words.

t t

table | lion | teddy

u u

umbrella | fish | unicorn

v v

violin | van | bird

w w

dog | window | watch

x x

xylophone | rabbit | x-ray

y y

yellow | yo-yo | sun

z z

butterfly | zip | zebra

Trace each capital letter and write the matching small one underneath it. The first one has been done for you.

| A B C D E F G H I J K L M |
| a b c d e f g h i j k l m |

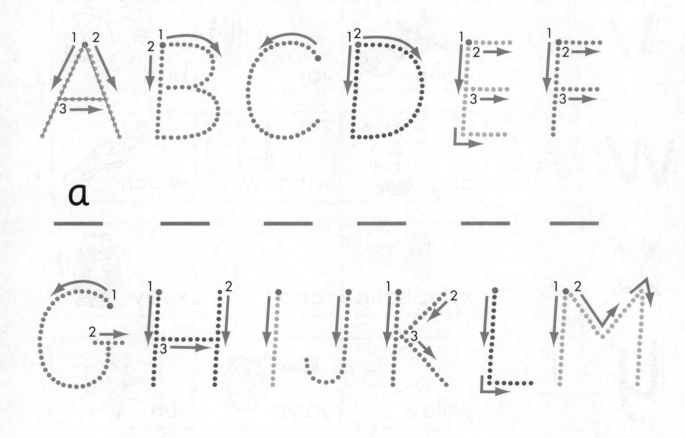

a

Note for parent: This activity helps children to recognize and write capital letters.

Names start with a capital letter. Write your name here:

N O P Q R S T U V W X Y Z

n o p q r s t u v w x y z

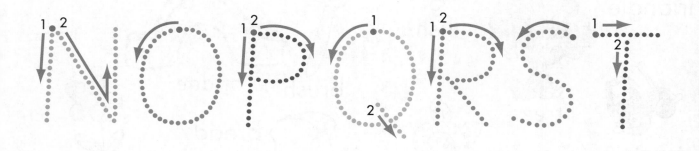

N O P Q R S T

– – – – – – – – – – –

U V W X Y Z

– – – – – – – – – – –

Blending sounds

Say the name of the picture in the middle of each group. Circle the things around it that begin with the same sound.

train

triangle

fish

tree

tractor

pig

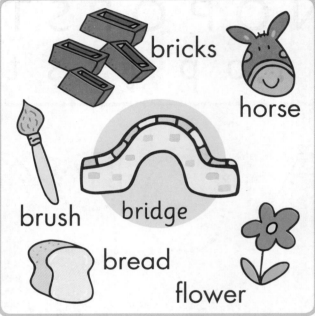

bricks

horse

brush

bridge

bread

flower

fly

flipper

flag

flower

cat

duck

Note for parent: When **t** and **r** join together they make **tr**, when **b** and **r** join together they make **br** and **f** and **l** make **fl**.

Choose a letter sound

Choose a letter to write at the start of each word.

f	h	t	b	k	z

_ish

_ird

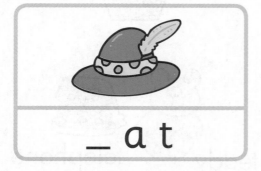

_at

_ing

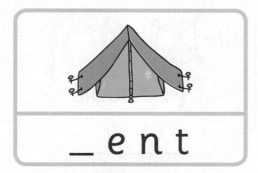

_ent

_ebra

Note for parent: This gives children the opportunity to choose and write hard consonant sounds and to build words.

13

Odd one out

Circle the odd one out in each group.

lion

kite

leaf

ladder

candle

cat

apple

comb

book

panda

pig

parachute

teddy

telephone

kite

table

Plurals

Write a label for each picture. Add an **s** to the end because there is more than 1 thing.

hat   _ _ _ _

sock   _ _ _ _ _

bat   _ _ _ _

ball   _ _ _ _ _

tree   _ _ _ _ _

star   _ _ _ _ _

Note for parent: This gives children the opportunity to choose and write hard consonant sounds and to build words.

15

Word endings

Say what each picture is, then choose a letter sound to write at the end of each word.

| s | g | d | n | t | k |

be_

do_

su_

boo_

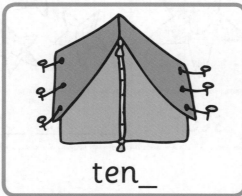

ten_

bu_

16

Rhyming words

Do these words rhyme? Put a ✔ or a ✖ in the box under each pair of pictures.

house   mouse

car   boat

sock   clock

moon   star

key   tree

box   fox

Note for parent: Make sure you say these words out loud so your child can hear the words that rhyme.

Make the words

Write in the missing letter sounds to make the words.

g n c w m b

_oat

rainbo_

quee_

dru_

_ake

_ook

Note for parent: This activity helps children to recognize the letters that make an individual word.

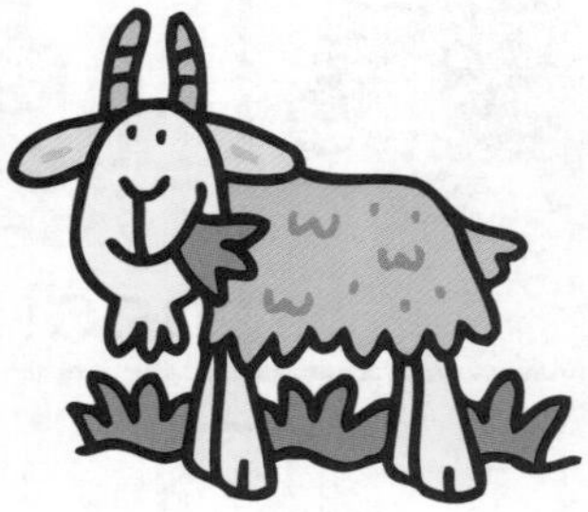

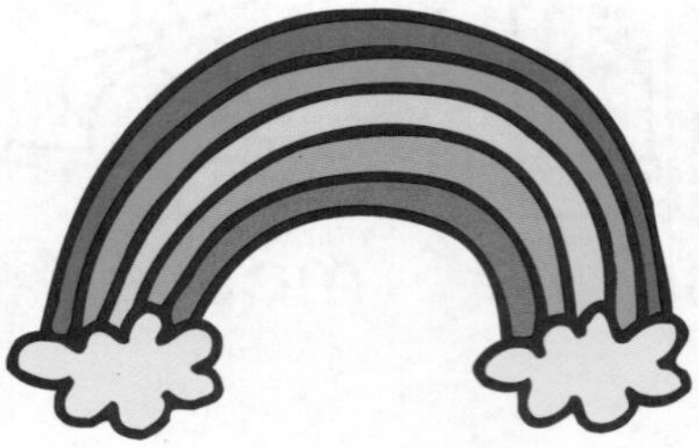

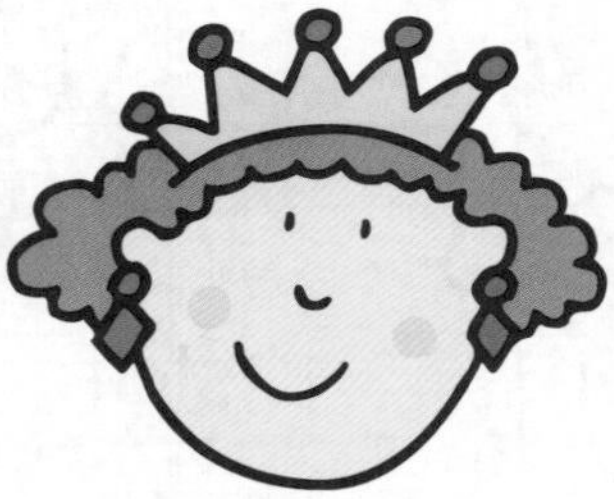

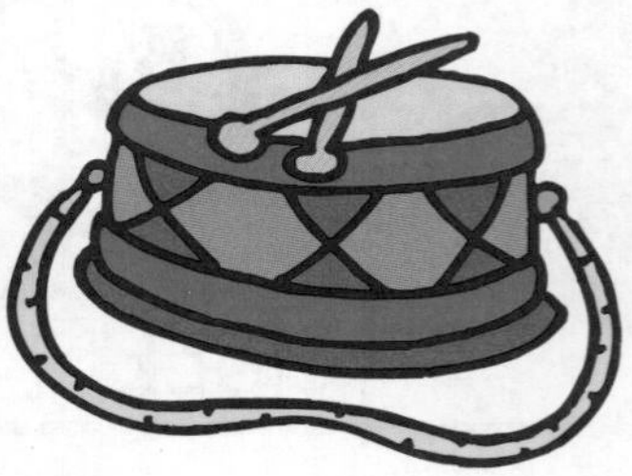

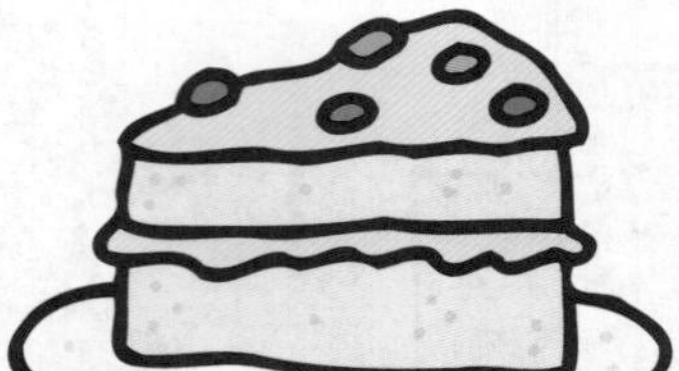

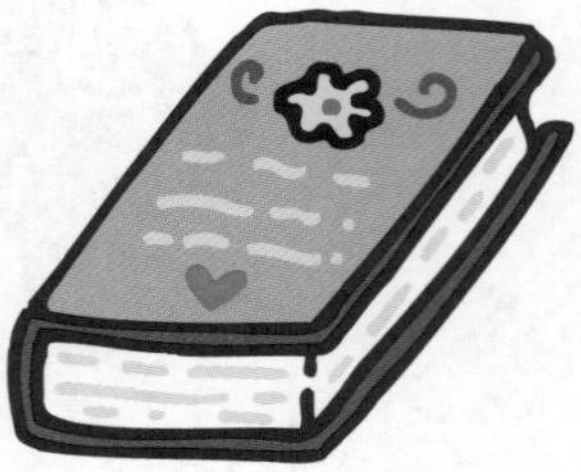

Quick quiz

Draw lines to join the words that rhyme.

hook

fan

dog

book

man

frog

Write a word next to each picture.

_ _ _

_ _ _

_ _ _

_ _ _

Note for parent: This is a revision of rhyme and simple consonant-vowel-consonant words.

Sounds in the middle

Trace over these letters and say the sounds.

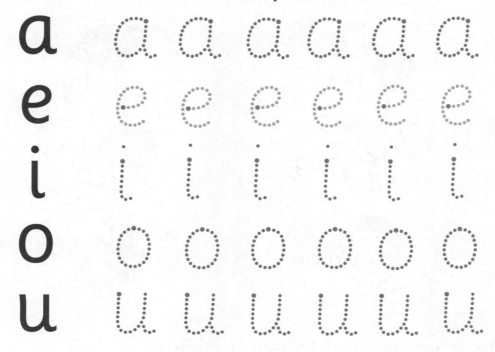

a   a a a a a a a

e   e e e e e e

i   i i i i i i i

o   o o o o o o o

u   u u u u u u u

Name each picture. Tick the words with an **a** sound in the middle.

Name each picture. Tick the words with an **e** sound in the middle.

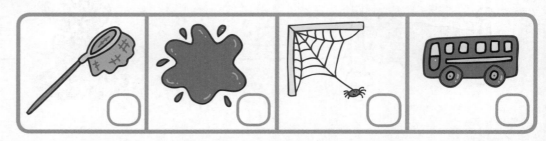

Note to parent: This activity helps children to identify the vowels **a**, **e**, **i**, **o** and **u**.

Name each picture. Tick the words with an **i** sound in the middle.

Name each picture. Tick the words with an **o** sound in the middle.

Name each picture. Tick the words with a **u** sound in the middle.

Make the sentences

Choose a word from this list to write into each sentence. Ask a grown-up to read each sentence out loud first.

and	in	into	at	I
he	she	am	to	can

The zebra looked __ the lion.

The fish jumped ____ the sea.

The cat ___ dog are friends.

Note for parent: This will help your child learn high-frequency words that they will need to help them write and read independently.

The birds sat __ the nest.

"_ am the queen and __ is the king."

"I __ the king and ___ is the queen."

"I like __ eat grass."

"I ___ fly!"

Answers

Pages 6–7

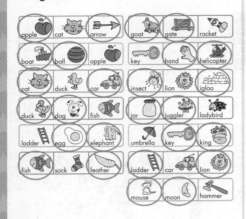

Pages 8–9

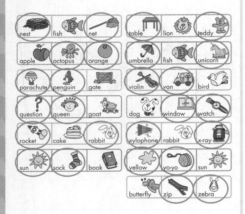

Page 12

tree: <u>tr</u>iangle, <u>tr</u>ain, <u>tr</u>actor
bridge: <u>br</u>ush, <u>br</u>ead, <u>br</u>icks
flower: <u>fl</u>ipper, <u>fl</u>y, <u>fl</u>ag

Page 13

<u>f</u>ish, <u>b</u>ird, <u>h</u>at, <u>k</u>ing, <u>t</u>ent, <u>z</u>ebra

Page 14

Page 15

hats, socks, bats, balls, trees, stars

Page 16

be<u>d</u>, do<u>g</u>, su<u>n</u>, boo<u>k</u>, ten<u>t</u>, bu<u>s</u>

Page 17

Page 18

goat, rainbo<u>w</u>, queen, dru<u>m</u>,
<u>c</u>ake, <u>b</u>ook

Page 19

hook/book, dog/frog, man/fan
hat, pig, bed, dog

Pages 20–21

Pages 22–23

The zebra looked <u>at</u> the lion.
The fish jumped <u>into</u> the sea.
The cat <u>and</u> dog are friends.
The birds sat <u>in</u> the nest.
"<u>I</u> am the queen and <u>he</u> is
the king."
"I <u>am</u> the king and <u>she</u> is
the queen."
"I like <u>to</u> eat grass."
"I <u>can</u> fly!"